PROFESSOR & POLLITÖ

For information contact info@rythehouse.com

Written by Alexandra Hewazy
Illustrated by Cory Reid
Designed by Stephanie Drake

Paperback ISBN: 978-1-7399061-0-8
Ebook ISBN: 978-1-7399061-1-5

www.rythehouse.com

Doodle Pad

Pollito is very excited today. He and Professor are going to Harry's birthday party. Harry is Pollito's best friend.

Professor and Pollito arrive at the party. All of Harry's friends are there.
Can you count how many dogs are at the party?

That's right, there are eight dogs at the party.

Bernard

Pollito

Sophie

Harry

Lenny

Penelope

Barry

Poppy

The first party game is pass the parcel. Pollito wins!
The prize is a doggy doughnut.

"Will you share that with me?" barks Harry. "It is my birthday after all".

Let me show you how you can share
that equally so you both get
the same amount.

There's only one doughnut but two hungry friends who want to eat it.

So, to make sure it is fair we need to split the doughnut into two equal parts so you both get the same amount. That's fair isn't it?

When we split a whole, like this whole doughnut, into equal parts we make a fraction.

A fraction shows us how many times we have split one item into equal parts. It helps us to share fairly with our friends.

So, we have one delicious doughnut and two hungry friends.

I am going to cut the doughnut down the middle so that we have two equal pieces.

Pollito finishes his half in one mouthful and runs off
to play chase with the other friends.

Do you remember how many dogs are at Harry's party?

That's right, eight dogs. But we only have one pizza – let's use fractions to make sure no one is left hungry.

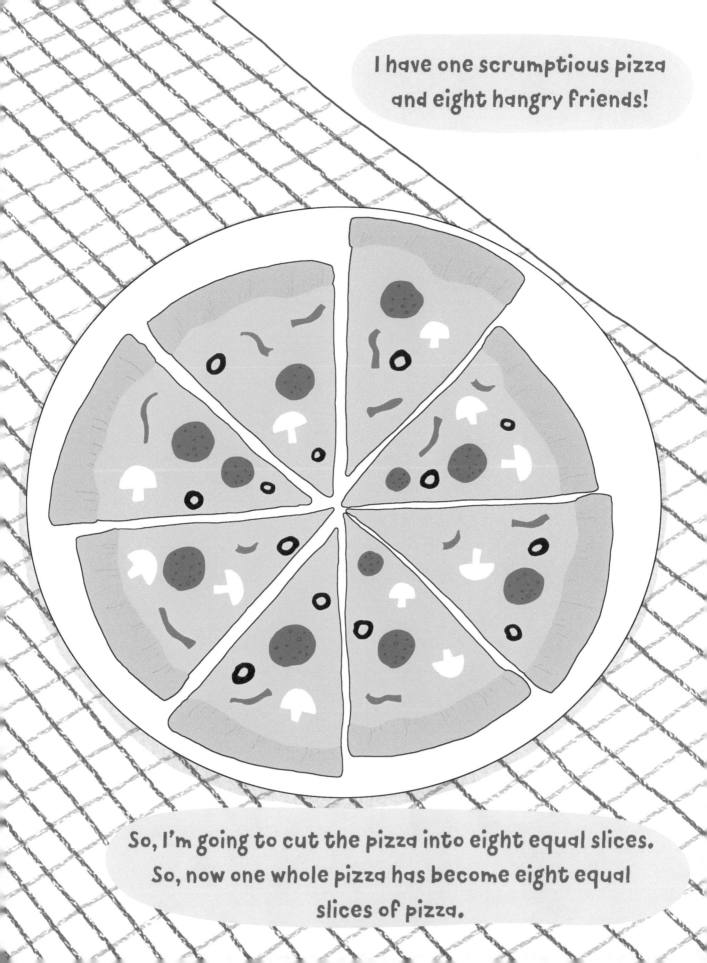

That's right, eight. We split the pizza into eight pieces. The number on the top shows how many of the eight slices each of the dogs have.

That's right, everyone has one slice.

So, the fraction is 1/8, or we call it one-eighth.

After lunch all the dogs play musical statues while Harry's mum prepares the birthday cakes.

Harry has two birthday cakes this year, one in the shape of a bone and one in the shape of a ball, because his two favourite things to do are searching for bones and chasing balls.

Pollito wants to gobble up all of the cake but he knows he should share with his friends. Henriette cuts the ball cake into four pieces. If Pollito takes one slice what fraction of the cake will he eat?

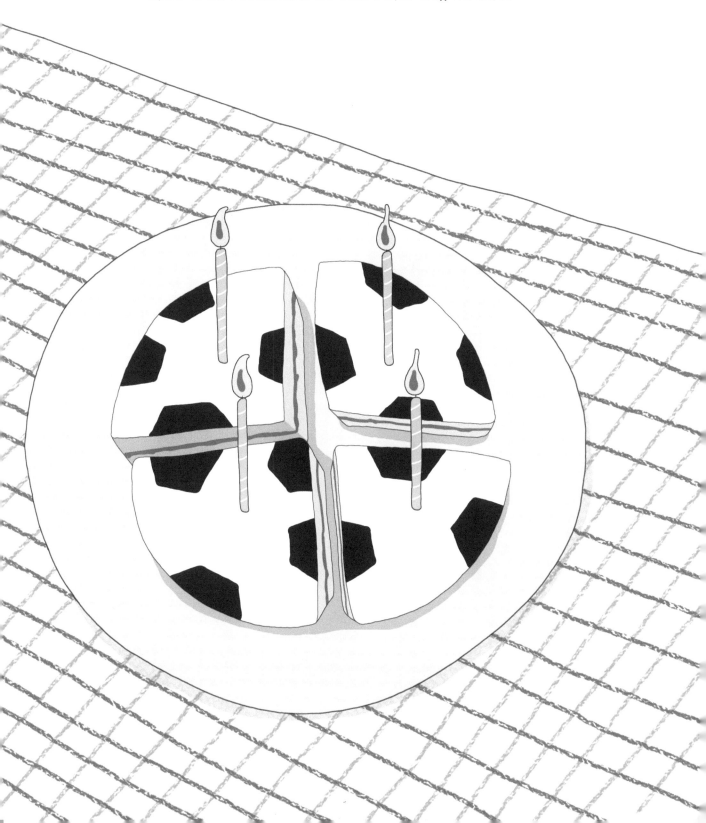

The party has finished and it is time to go home now.
Bernard, Sophie, and Penelope are the first to leave.

Henriette gives a party bag to each dog as they leave.
She has got five bags left.

Do you know what fraction of dogs are left?

YES!

YOU DID IT, POLLITO!

After all the excitment of fractions... and the party food,
Pollito goes home for a well-earned snooze.

The End

Lightning Source UK Ltd.
Milton Keynes UK
UKHW050412120921
390384UK00003B/113